The Adventures of
Ray and Sam
And The Rainy Day

Written by: Reggie Williams
Illustrated by: TullipStudio

Dedicate

This book is dedicated to Robin Williams, Myla Williams, Reggie Williams Jr, Janie Williams and Reginald Williams.

Growing Up

Ray and Sam Did Everything Together

"

While both boys make A's and B's

Ray is Hardworking while Sam does not like to work hard

"

"

**Both Graduate
from High School**

Go to College And Get

Good Jobs

"

" Ray and Sam Get Paid

Working for the Yola Cola Gaming Company "

Ray is wise with his money

Spends very little money and puts the majority of his money in the bank. This will help pay for needs that come up unexpectedly

Ray Enjoys Going To the Bank

and has a Savings account, Stocks, and a Savings bond. All of these items will help Ray make additional money.

Sam is not wise with his money

Sam spends all his money. He spends money on fancy clothes, expensive cars, and vacations. He does not have any money left to pay for needs that come up unexpectedly

"After the Tornado, the company closes and does not pay Ray and Sam for several months"

Because Ray saved
his money from
working he was able
to pay all his bills and
still stay happy

"Because Sam did not save his money.

He had to sale his cars, jewelry and big house so he could pay his bills "

It became so bad for Sam, that he eventually had to move in with Ray. And pay Ray rent.

When Yola Cola Company
finally opened again,
Sam decided to save as
much money as he could

Always remember.....
Save your money for A
Rainy Day.....

About The Author

Growing up my parents instilled the value of hard work and the importance of managing my money at a very early age. Now after working in finance for several years I would like to help others start the first conversations of finance.